ESSENTIAL HYPERTENSION AS ADAPTATION TO EXCESS GRAVITATIONAL STRESS: INTEGRATING CONCEPT FOR COMPLETE PREVENTION

ESSENTIAL HYPERTENSION AS ADAPTATION TO EXCESS GRAVITATIONAL STRESS: INTEGRATING CONCEPT FOR COMPLETE PREVENTION

STANISLAV E. PEKARSKI

Nova Science Publishers, Inc.
New York

NOTICE TO THE READER

LIBRARY OF CONGRESS CATALOGING-IN-PUBLICATION DATA
Available upon request

ISBN 1-59454-604-5

Published by Nova Science Publishers, Inc. ✣ New York

CONTENTS

PREFACE

Space flight studies have demonstrated that adaptation to gravitational stress after prolonged microgravity includes sympathetic activation, water retention, and arterial pressure increase, i.e., a process very similar to development of essential hypertension, which from this perspective looks like an advanced stage of that adaptation with sympathetic hyperactivity, vasoconstriction, volume overload, and arterial hypertension in case of some further increase in gravitational stress.

This book contains theoretical analysis of human cardiovascular function in real conditions of Earth gravitational field leading to the scientifically sound hypothesis of essential hypertension as advanced stage of natural adaptation of the human cardiovascular system to abnormally increased gravitational stress associated with modern "sitting" lifestyle. Also clinical and experimental data are presented supporting this hypothesis according to comprehensive literature search.

In upright position gravitation shifts blood downwards emptying upper body and reducing blood supply to the brain. Passively filling heart cannot pump blood out of the lower into the upper body. Compensation is provided through lower body vasoconstriction and circulating volume increase. The gravitational stress (GS) in the cardiovascular system in an upright position may be defined as amount of work necessary to return the blood upward and maintain adequate upper-body circulation calculated as the product of the gravitational potential (Ugr=g*h) and the mass of blood shifted by gravitation: GS=U*Mshift. In a complex vascular network, this blood shift is actually a function of time, estimated in a first approximation as Mshift(t)=(Ugr*t)/Rd (Rd: the resistance to downward blood flow) so that gravitational stress is proportional to the time spent upright GS=U*Mshift(t)=(Ugr2*t)/Rd=(g2*h2*t)/Rd. From this analysis typical for modern life regular, prolonged sitting should cause a significant increase in gravitational stress in the cardiovascular system, requiring advanced antigravitational response with sympathetic hyperactivity, vasoconstriction, volume overload, and arterial hypertension. The hypertensive effect of prolonged sitting has been directly demonstrated in several clinical studies. Numerous population studies demonstrated higher prevalence of hypertension for occupations with predominantly sitting posture during worktime.

Thus, essential hypertension in scientifically sound way is explained as adaptation to increased gravitational stress resulted from modern "sitting" lifestyle. This gravitational hypothesis of essential hypertension fully integrates two existed major concepts of sympathetic hyperactivity and abnormal sodium reabsorption as complementary mechanisms of antigravitational response but contrary to them offers a way to complete healing of the disease through elimination of the primary factor of abnormal gravitational stress.

INTRODUCTION

Hypertension literally means abnormally high tension. In narrow sense as a cardiovascular disorder hypertension denotes abnormally high tension in arterial part of the cardiovascular system. However, it is not the whole story.

Excessive tension damages cardiovascular system and causes cardiovascular complications like myocardial infarction, stroke, heart failure responsible for the most part of death and disability in industrial world. Attributed to hypertension excess in cardiovascular morbidity and mortality creates an extremely heavy burden on modern societies, their economical and healthcare system.

According to the latest data from NHANES (2002), about 65 million people in the United States have hypertension (systolic blood pressure [SBP] >/= 140 mm Hg or diastolic blood pressure (DBP) >/= 90 mm Hg, taking antihypertensive medication, or being diagnosed with hypertension on 2 occasions). This represents a 30% increase over the previous survey for 1988-1994. The prevalence of hypertension is highest among African Americans (26.7%) and American or Alaska Natives (25.0%) and lowest among Asians (13.5%). The prevalence in white Americans is 20.1%. The prevalence of hypertension in the total population is higher among women than men (32.8% vs. 31.5%). Among the age group < 55 years, the prevalence is higher in men, but after this age, the prevalence becomes much higher in women.

Hypertension was listed as a primary or contributing cause of death in about 261,000 of about 2.4 million US deaths in 2002. This represents a 57% increase in deaths from hypertension over the previous decade.

As a result of the increased prevalence of hypertension in the US population, the estimated total direct and indirect cost of hypertension of

2005(when this book was written) is almost $60 billion, of which two thirds ($44.2) represent direct costs, such as hospitals, physicians, and medications. The indirect costs represent lost productivity resulting from morbidity and mortality. The total cost for cardiovascular disease and stroke for 2005 is estimated to be $393.5 billion [1].

This picture is typical for industrial world and is supposed to only get worse in the future. Recent analysis of the data reporting sex-specific and age-specific prevalence of hypertension in representative population samples during last two decades revealed unfavorable trend in hypertension prevalence. (Authors searched the published literature from Jan 1, 1980, to Dec 31, 2002, using MEDLINE, supplemented by a manual search of bibliographies of retrieved articles. They included studies that reported sex-specific and age-specific prevalence of hypertension in representative population samples. All data were obtained independently by two investigators with a standardised protocol and data-collection form).

Overall, 26.4% (95% CI 26.0-26.8%) of the adult population in 2000 had hypertension (26.6% of men [26.0-27.2%] and 26.1% of women [25.5-26.6%]), and 29.2% (28.8-29.7%) were projected to have this condition by 2025 (29.0% of men [28.6-29.4%] and 29.5% f women [29.1-29.9%]). The estimated total number of adults with hypertension in 2000 was 972 million (957-987 million); 333 million (329-336 million) in economically developed countries and 639 million (625-654 million) in economically developing countries. The number of adults with hypertension in 2025 was predicted to increase by about 60% to a total of 1.56 billion (1.54-1.58 billion) [2].

Treatment of such a great army of hypertensive people requires enormous efforts and resources. The worst thing is that even if best available today treatment will be administered to all hypertensives without exclusion (ideal situation) the problem of hypertension will not be solved because contemporary treatment neither stops hypertension, nor cause any temporal remission of it but only partly reduces its complications. If aforementioned death rate from hypertension in US in 2002 (i.e., after years of functioning of national antihypertensive program (NBEP) and abundance of available antihypertensive drugs) is applied to the predicted number of hypertensives in 2025 we will receive about 6.264 millions of deaths worldwide caused by hypertension despite active treatment.

Thus, it is hardly to overestimate the problem of hypertension for modern world. Hypertension today is not just excessive tension in the cardiovascular system it is excessive tension of the whole world.

* Address for correspondence about the manuscript: Stanislav E. Pekarski, Russia 634028 Tomsk, Moscowski Tract 62 app. 11. Telephone Home: +7(3822)416367, Cell: +79138233527; E-mail: Pekarski@cardio.tsu.ru, Pekarski@mail2000.ru

Chapter 1

Currently Available Antihypertensive Treatment Cannot Solve the Hypertension Problem

Approximately a 50-year history of development of treatment of hypertension has resulted in a great variety of antihypertensive drugs available today for decrease of blood pressure in hypertensive patients. Regardless of their chemical structure and mechanism of action all antihypertensive drugs seem to have equal effect on blood pressure - average decrease of 10/5 mmHg for grade 1 hypertension and 20/10 mmHg in patients with higher grades [3]. All of those drugs were developed for only one purpose - to low blood pressure, i.e., to relieve one major symptom of the disease and not to stop underlying pathological process causing high blood pressure. Therefore, antihypertensive drugs are nothing more than purely symptomatic treatment.

What are major characteristics of the current pharmacological treatment of hypertension?

1. Contemporary treatment of essential hypertension with blood pressure lowering drugs neither heals patients from the disease nor causes any temporary remission of it and, therefore, must be administered for the rest of the patient's life without any hope to stop medication.
2. This lifelong administration of expensive chemicals rarely brings sensible improvement to the usually asymptomatic hypertensive patients, while it frequently causes various adverse effects.

3. The only benefit of this treatment is the prevention of approximately 20% of major cardiovascular complications (22% by regimens based on ACE inhibitors, 18% by regimens based on calcium antagonists, with no significant differences between regimens based on ACE inhibitors, calcium antagonists, or diuretics or beta blockers [4]).

Such low effective treatment, however, for years remains accepted as the best option for hypertensive patients. Yet the very fact that hypotensive drugs must be taken without ceasing to the end of the patient's life demonstrates their inability to affect the course of the diseases. Another fact about contemporary pharmacological treatment of hypertension is that in order to demonstrate the actual benefit of the treatment in reduction of the cardiovascular complications it is necessary to perform very large clinical studies and treat thousands of the patients for many years. If it is so difficult to show the effect of the treatment, obviously this effect is very small.

This situation when no etiology (i.e., really effective treatment capable of solving hypertension problem) is available and symptomatic interventions are the only choice for hypertensive patients, the result then is a chronic failure of medical science to identify primary cause – etiology of essential hypertension.

Etiology of essential hypertension has been a mystery so long that finally there appeared a concept of essential hypertension as a multifactor disease, i.e., without any primary cause at all and, therefore, without any hope to find disease-terminating etiological treatment capable to completely free patients from the disease. This thesis has extremely serious consequences for hypertensive patients because it establishes the current, low-effective strategy of hypotensive drug treatment as the best option once and for all, burying any further attempt to find really effective etiological interventions. Having no actual proofs except a lack of counter-arguments, this thesis of the multifactor origin of essential hypertension has laid a solid foundation for lifelong use of hypotensive drugs as the only possible treatment of hypertension to the joy of pharmaceutical industry. However, the truth is that all currently suggested components of the multifactor model of essential hypertension have been found to account for only a small part of arterial pressure variability (e.g. a polymorphism in the angiotensinogen gene accounts for <6% of it) [2] and cannot explain development of stable and significant arterial hypertension in the middle age. Yet, this idea even being without real proofs has made its evil work. The very hope to find a cause of essential hypertension seems to almost die today.

As a result, development of hypertension treatment has never changed its major focus on this low effective way of temporal lowering of blood pressure. Each decade several new medications for treatment of hypertension are registered as a result of spending millions of dollars in the hypotensive drug research and development. They may differ significantly chemically and in all other aspects except one – all of them may only temporally reduce arterial pressure to some extent and never stop the hypertension. To compete with older drugs new ones are often claimed to have additional benefits beyond blood pressure decrease. For example, angiotensin converting enzyme inhibitors - ACEIs and angiotensin receptor blockers - ARBs are usually considered as having renoprotective and cardioprotective effects independent of blood pressure decrease. Yet there is still no truly significant evidence that one drug is better than the other for the treatment of hypertension. It is remarkable that almost all studies assessing those additional benefits of the antihypertensive drugs easily find them in the new drugs and almost never in the old. Therefore, it is not clear whether those benefits are real or just a smartly designed promotion.

Conclusion is not very optimistic. Contemporary course on symptomatic treatment unable to affect the course of the disease actually is a way to cultivate hypertension and not to eliminate it. The direct evidence of this paradoxical effect is that population of hypertensives increases despite highly developed and easily available hypotensive treatment. While this course perfectly meets interests of pharmaceutical industry (increasing army of lifelong consumers guarantee high sales and profits) it is of little benefit for patients and society as a whole. Yet, there is almost no attempt to change the situation. The transformation of the basic understanding of essential hypertension as the disease of unknown etiology/cause into concept of multifactor disease further reduces chances that medical science will ever discover the primary cause of essential hypertension and find effective treatments of the disease in the future.

Chapter 2

QUADRUPEDAL HUMANS OR WHY CARDIOVASCULAR RESEARCHERS HAVE NEVER HAD A CHANCE TO FIND A PRIMARY CAUSE OF ESSENTIAL HYPERTENSION

Chronic failure to clarify the pathogenesis of essential hypertension obviously points to the fundamental limitations of the approaches used so far to study human cardiovascular system. What are these limitations? Years of experiments with either quadrupedal laboratory animals or mechanical models/combined preparations constructed in the horizontal plane have had a profound impact on the minds of cardiovascular researchers. After years of studying the cardiovascular system in horizontal plane they developed a "horizontal" way of thinking about the cardiovascular system, completely ignoring gravitation because the vertical force of gravity has a little effect on circulation in horizontal plane. Yet 2/3 of the time (daytime) the human cardiovascular system functions in the upright position when gravitation poses to it a serious challenge a to keep sufficient amount of blood in the upper parts of the body. In this typical for human body vertical position the classical experimental design used by Arthur Guyton and his group [3] to develop modern cardiovascular physiology simply will not work. In fact, the very reason why the researchers posed their experimental preparations in horizontal plane – because those models could not work in vertical position, i.e., were absolutely inadequate for the study of human hemodynamics. In essence, contemporary cardiovascular physiology sees humans as quadrupeds like mice or rats never questioning how in human cardiovascular system blood is lifted up from the feet to the heart against the force of gravity in upright posture not just for a while but for most of the time. This fundamentally wrong approach leaves the scientists without any chance to find the true cause of hypertension in the uprightly living humans.

Gravitation is a major factor of our environment. It is a fundamental property of the universe. Yet gravitation has no place in cardiovascular science and has never been taken into account in cardiovascular research. There is almost no mention of gravitation in the models of pathogenesis of cardiovascular diseases. In fact, despite four centuries passed since Isaac Newton published his brilliant work, *Principia* and presented to the world gravitational theory, the cardiovascular scientists has not yet discovered gravitation. They should be prescribed to spend less time in labs and more outside sitting under the apple trees.

Chapter 3

SPACE FLIGHT STUDIES – DISCOVERING STRESSFUL EFFECT OF EARTH'S GRAVITATION ON HUMAN CARDIOVASCULAR SYSTEM

The inadequate experimental approach had blinded scientific thinking so much that it took launching a man into space in order to discover the fact that gravitation imposes severe stress on the human cardiovascular system. Removal of gravitation during space flight causes feet-to-head blood shift within cardiovascular system manifested in the two visible changes. The first is a swelling of the head ("puffy head" syndrome), and the second is a decrease in the circumference of the legs ("bird-legs" syndrome). Feet-to-head shift of blood within the cardiovascular system leads to increase of blood volume and pressure in the vessels of the upper body. High hydrostatic pressure in the vascular bed of the upper body causes excessive transcapillary fluid move and swelling in these regions including head. Emptying the lower parts of the body causes decrease of blood volume in these regions and, thereby, decrease of volume and circumference of legs. Volume overloading of the upper body with increase of blood pressure in heart chambers, central and intracranial arteries and veins is sensed as hypervolemic state and responded by reduction of plasma volume, decrease of sympathetic activity, arterial pressure, and cardiac mass, i.e., obvious relaxation of the cardiovascular system. Return to Earth's gravitation causes the completely opposite changes - blood shift to the lower body in upright position that leads to volume overloading of peripheral vascular system of the pelvis and legs and emptying of the upper body and central part of the cardiovascular system positioned in that region. Decrease of blood supply to the brain results in development of orthostatic intolerance early after landing.

Decrease of blood volume and pressure in the heart, central and intracranial arteries and veins is sensed as hypovolemic state and responded by an sympathoexcitation, vasoconstriction and activation of the fluid retention system followed by increases in circulating volume, arterial pressure and cardiac work, i.e., obvious stress in the cardiovascular system [5, 6, 7, 8, 9, 10, 11]. Similar changes in the cardiovascular system have been found with prolonged bed rest (simulated microgravity), indicating that it is the upright position that plays a key role in gravitational stress.

Chapter 4

BASICS OF PHYSICAL THEORY OF GRAVITATION

To understand the nature of the effect that Earth's gravitational field has on human cardiovascular system one needs first to gain at least basic knowledge of physical theory of gravitation.

Gravitation is a universal property of all material objects to attract each other. This property of attraction by nature is an action at a distance, i.e., does not require direct contact between objects but is exerted over a significant distance between them. In physics such action-at-a-distance is typically described with force-field concept allowing its easy quantitative estimation. Suppose, for example, we have two objects A and B at a distance r. The object A attracts object B. Object A produces a force that acts on object B at a distance r and pulls it in the direction of the object A. This attracting force is proportional to the masses of the objects and inversely proportional to the squared distance between them

$$F=G*M_a*M_b/r^2, \qquad (1)$$

where G is the universal gravitational constant, M_a and M_b are masses of the objects A and B respectively, r - distance between them.

If we move object B in a new location it will be still attracted by the object A but power of this attraction will change with the change of the distance r between them. Thus, the fundamental nature of this property is that object A attracts object B, i.e., produces force acting on it, at any point in the space. This is described as object A creates a vector field so that each point in the space is associated with vector of attracting force produced by the objects A that would act on object B if it were positioned at this point. As it mentioned above the attracting force is dependent on the mass of object B.

To generalize this description of the property of the object A to attract material objects we need to make definition of the force vector independent of mass of object B. This is done through dividing attracting force by the mass of object B. The resulting force has the meaning of unit force, i.e., force acting on object of unit mass and is usually denoted by the letter g.

$$g=G*M_a/r^2 \qquad (2)$$

Now we have introduced the term of unit gravitational force that does not depend on the mass of attracted object B but depends on the mass of the object A generating the field and a distance r. If gravitational force is not counteracted it causes an object to move in the direction of the field and does a work proportional to the distance of that move W=F*S, where F is force of gravity and S is moving distance.

This means there is an energy stored in the gravitational field that comes out of storage as work done by the field in moving material objects. This energy is called gravitational potential energy. The work done by the gravitational field in moving objects does not depend on trajectory of the movement but only on the component of movement along the direction of the field. The gravitational force moves objects until the distance between them is zero when the force is also zero. Quantitative estimation of the energy conserved in gravitational field is done using concept of gravitational potential. Again normalization is used to provide a measure of the energy conserved in the gravitational field independent from the objects it acts on. The gravitational potential or potential energy of the gravitational field at any point is equal to the work done by the field in moving unit mass from that point to the center of the field. For any two points at different distances r_1, r_2 ($r_1<>r_2$) from a center of the field there is a gradient of the gravitational potential, which is equal to the amount of work done by the gravitational field in moving unit mass between these points.

Thus, if an object has spatial distribution of masses there is always a gradient of the gravitational potential across the object. If the unit gravity force does not significantly changes across the object then gradient of the gravitational potential is equal to the product of unit gravity force g and dimension of the object along the direction of the field.

$$U_{gr}=g*r, \qquad (3)$$

where r is dimension of the object in the direction of the field.

If the unit gravity force changes significantly across the object then actual value of the gravitational potential is obtained by integration of unit gravity force across that object.

$$U_{gr}=\int g*dr \quad (4)$$

Chapter 5

CARDIOVASCULAR SYSTEM IN GRAVITATIONAL FIELD

Earth as a large object creates powerful gravitational field strong enough to keep so big object like a moon in stationary orbit not allowing it to fly in the space. Though gravitation is a property of all material objects for any relatively small object near the Earth the gravitational force produced by the planet is much more than gravitational force produced by the object so the latter may be neglected in this situation.

Cardiovascular system is a closed tubular net filled with free circulating liquid – blood. On the surface of the Earth its powerful gravitational field attracts the free particles of the blood in the cardiovascular system to the center of the field. As long as these blood particles are free within the system they have to move in the direction of the field. The effect of Earth's gravitational field on the human cardiovascular system is similar to the effect of an electric field on a conductor. Like an electric field moves free electrons within a conductor, the gravitational field moves blood (free particles) within the cardiovascular system.

The effect of the electric field on a conductor is proportional to the gradient of electric potential across the conductor. In analogy the effect of the gravitational field on cardiovascular system is proportional to the gradient of the gravitational potential across the system. According to the theory of gravitational physics this gradient is equal to work done by the field in moving a unit mass of blood across the system in the direction of the field $U_{gr} = g \times r$. The direction of Earth's gravitational field near its surface is vertical, and the distance r is equal to the vertical dimension or height h of the system: $U_{gr} = g \times h$. This explains why the effect of gravitation is significant in the upright position only. In the horizontal position, vertical dimension of the human body, h, is rather small, making U_{gr} negligible, but it increases multifold in upright posture.

If a conductor is not a closed circuit electric field moves negatively charged electrons to the one of the ends of the conductor that gains a negative charge while another end remaining without electrons gains a positive charge. Therefore, a new gradient of electric potential (internal electric field) is created that is opposite to that initially imposed by the external field. The move of electrons goes until a point of equilibrium between external and internal fields when induced gradient of gravitational potential is equal to the gradient imposed by the external field. That is the effect of electric field on a conductor faces counteraction from the conductor so that finally a new equilibrium state is created when action is equal to counteraction.

In a close analogy to the above when Earth's gravitational field moves blood to the lower end of the body in upright posture it faces counteraction from the cardiovascular system. This counteraction is increasing elastic vascular resistance. Volume overloading of vessels in the lower parts of the body causes their additional extension and proportional increase of elastic forces of vascular walls counteracting this distension. Increase of elastic forces of vascular walls in the vessels of the lower parts of the body produces greater intravascular pressure and a pressure gradient is created in the cardiovascular system counteracting downward blood move. The more blood is moved by gravitation into vessels of the lower parts of the body the more is this counteraction. Finally, the process of blood redistribution stops when the induced hydrostatic pressure gradient equals gradient of the gravitational potential. In upright posture mean arterial pressure in the feet raises to about 200 mmHg as compared to nearly 100 mmHg in supine position.

Within the body the gravitational potential is maximal at its top and gradually decreases downward to its lowest point. Hydrostatic pressure induced by gravitation in the cardiovascular system, on the contrary, is minimal at the top of the body and gradually increases downward. When equilibrium between gravitational blood shift and counteracting vascular resistance is reached a gradient of the gravitational potential between the top of the body and any point across the body is equal to the gradient of the intravascular hydrostatic pressure between the same points taken with negative sign. This means that induced hydrostatic pressure gradient mirrors gradient of the gravitational potential, i.e., also gradually increases from the top of the body in the head-to-feet direction.

With accumulation of the blood in the lower parts of the body less blood volume circulates in the upper body and is supplied to its organs, first of all to the brain. In fact, this gravitation-induced downward blood redistribution in upright posture, if not prevented causes critical decrease of blood supply to the brain and development of syncope or fainting. This phenomenon is extensively studied in the patients with congenital connective tissue disorders and also in patients with autonomic failure. Former disorders affects structural organization of vascular walls, i.e., passive component of their elastic resistance to the distension while the latter – vascular tone, which is an active component of the vascular resistance. As a result of decreased elastic vascular resistance there is less counteraction to the gravitation induced blood shift in vertical posture so that significantly more blood redistributes downward. The patients quickly developed syncope in upright posture and this condition is referred to as orthostatic intolerance. Another example of the syncope due to excessive redistribution of blood into the lower pats of the body is loss of consciousness experienced by pilots during +Gz flight maneuvers when they experience powerful head-to-feet force, which is several times higher than normal gravitational force in upright posture.

Thus, Earth's gravitation has so powerful an effect on the human cardiovascular function in the upright position of the body that if not prevented causes severe circulatory insufficiency with development of deep ischemia of the upper body and the brain. In order to effectively function under such a great stress there must be a powerful antigravitational response of the cardiovascular system – adaptive changes of the system providing sufficient circulation in the upper body despite the powerful effect of Earth gravitation.

Chapter 6

ANTIGRAVITATIONAL RESPONSE OF THE CARDIOVASCULAR SYSTEM

To understand the mechanism of antigravitational response of the cardiovascular system we need to look at the circulation from the standpoint of gravitational physics or more exactly - to apply physical theory of gravitation to the concept of cardiovascular physiology.

First of all it should be noted that cardiovascular physiology has been radically changed in the second half of XX century. In fact, conventional cardiovascular physiology has been replaced by a completely new concept based on the original experimental work.

Contemporary cardiovascular physiology has been developed by Dr. Arthur Guyton in 50s of XXth century. It is remarkable that he has done this trying to do the same thing - find primary cause of hypertension.

He actually had to develop a principally new cardiovascular physiology because trying to understand a cause of hypertension he faced a great number of questions about cardiovascular function that had no answer in conventional wisdom. In order to answer the primary question - what causes high blood pressure he had to answer all those questions as well. Though finally he did not discover primary cause of hypertension his outstanding work produced new effective concept of cardiovascular function.

According to the conventional understanding of cardiovascular physiology since the heart is the organ, which actually pumps blood through the circulation, it seems logical to assume that the activity of the heart is the primary factor controlling systemic flow rate. However, such conclusion is typically contradicted by the data from experimental and clinical studies:

- In experimental animals and humans, it has been demonstrated that greatly increasing cardiac pumping by increasing heart rate with no change in the peripheral circulation does not appreciably increase cardiac output and systemic flow rate.

- Replacing the heart in experimental animals with a powerful artificial pump does not increase the "cardiac" output and flow rate.

In the 50s, Arthur Guyton came with the concept of "permissive" heart that easily explained numerous experimental and clinical data contradicting the conventional wisdom. His concept stated that the heart would pump only what was delivered to it through the veins, i.e., fills passively. He based it on the fact that when body tissues need extra blood flow to carry required oxygen and other nutrients, the blood vessels in those tissues expand or dilate, to allow increased flow. The control of cardiac output, he decided, was vested in the periphery.

The core principle of this generally supported today concept of circulation is that the heart is very unusual type of pump. The heart, like the urinary bladder, does not suck to fill, but on the contrary fills passively and produces circulation by ejecting whatever fluid enters it at diastole. During normal function, the heart not only doesn't develop a pressure negative to the intrathoracic pressure, but it offers an impediment to filling because of its limited volume-pressure compliance.

The evidence that the heart fills passively is provided by the data from heart catheterizations. Catheterization data shows end-diastolic pressure of five to ten centimeters of water above intrathoracic pressure. In fact, as ventricles fill, they not only do not suck, but they offer an increasing impediment to filling, as noted by the progressive increase in pressure toward the end of diastole. Negative ventricular pressure, in relation to intrathoracic pressure, has not been found in physiologic states. The negative pressure of inspiration, transmitted to the heart, should not be confused as the heart sucking. It is the chest that can suck, and not the heart. The heart, like all other muscles in the body, expends energy and does work by contracting. It cannot actively elongate its fibers to suck in a stroke volume. The heart itself has no ability to actively increase its chambers. For example the thorax has muscles fixed with one end to the ribs and with the other end - to the spinal column so that fixation to the spine is several centimeters higher then fixation to the rib. Contraction of these muscles pulls ribs upward distending thorax and increasing thoracic cavity. Such tricky organization is necessary that contraction may produce distension. There are no such muscles for the heart that were fixed to some external points, e.g. spine, so that contraction of those muscles may distend the heart and increase its chambers. It is distended passively by blood filling it under positive pressure. It is interesting that so obvious a conclusion regarding the inability of hollow muscle organ to actively increase its inner space/cavity for centuries remained a hidden mystery for cardiovascular science.

For a pump that cannot suck to fill, there must be a positive pressure at the inlets that blood may run into the ventricles and be pumped out. This pressure must be higher than diastolic pressure in the ventricles and also must be created independently of the heart. The primary cause of such background positive pressure in the circular system is elastic resistance of vascular walls to the distension caused by filling the system with significant volume of blood. Distension of circular vascular walls produces elastic forces trying to keep the initial perimeter of the walls and proportional to the increase of the perimeter, i.e., degree of the distension. These elastic forces of vascular walls are directed inside of the vessel to the geometrical center of the lumen and in this sense are compressing forces. The elastic forces of the distended vascular walls compress blood and produce positive pressure inside of the system. The magnitude of these forces are proportional to the degree of the distension and also to physical properties of the walls, i.e., is a function of vascular compliance and circulating volume

$$P=k*(V/C) \quad (5)$$

where k is coefficient, C-compliance and V-volume of blood

The vascular compliance includes passive component of structural organization and active component of vascular tone.

Passive component is a carcass built of connective tissue with elastic properties. Active component is a contraction of spirally positioned smooth muscle cells of vascular walls that makes vascular compliance **modifiable in wide range**. Modifiable nature of vascular compliance is unique property of cardiovascular system and as it will be shown below a key factor of controlling systemic flow rate and cardiovascular function. Modification of vascular compliance leads to correspondent modification of background positive pressure in the cardiovascular system and thereby filling of the non-sucking heart pump.

With a positive pressure in the cardiovascular system the heart may pump blood out and produce output. When blood is ejected into the arterial side of the circle, arterial pressure increases and a pressure gradient is created across the vascular circle (within the range of positive values). This gradient causes blood to flow around the circle back to the ventricular inlets.

In this sense the heart does not create positive pressure in the cardiovascular system itself, but rather distributes the pressure that is already created by the vascular walls.

During systole the contracting heart compress the blood that is within it. Intraventricular pressure raises and systolic ventricle-to-aorta pressure gradient is created. Blood moves following this gradient, output valves opens and stroke volume is displaced from the ventricle to aorta with proportional increase of aortal pressure. During diastole heart muscles relax and intracardiac pressure falls. A reverse pressure gradient is created between aorta and ventricle chamber causing blood to move back into ventricle. At the very beginning of this backward move output valves close and prevent further backward blood flow. Therefore, blood has to follow the diastolic aorta-to-ventricle pressure gradient alternatively through systemic circle. With blood flow the pressure gradually falls around the circle from maximal in aorta to minimal in the central veins. Remaining pressure gradient between venous end of the vascular circle and ventricular chamber - filling or input pressure – is the moving force for blood to enter the heart. The higher the filling pressure the more blood enters ventricle and is pumped out. Therefore, filling pressure controls cardiac output. The filling pressure directly depends on the blood volume returned from venous system.

In other words, the heart pump does not actively take a stroke volume of blood from veins and push it into arteries but on the contrary passively transports into arteries whatever is brought to it by the venous system. This situation is not the case in mechanical systems typically used to illustrate and understand the hemodynamics. In rigid impermeable mechanical systems with constant lumen and therefore capacity all fluid that is pushed into one end of the system finally comes to another end. In such systems the pumping device regardless of whether it fills actively or passively always fully controls systemic flow rate and maintains circulation. A unique feature of the vascular system is its ability to change their compliance and, therefore, diameter at any point around the system in order to adjust blood supply to the varying tissue demands with corresponding changes of total capacity of the system. This makes a difference for the pump with passive filling. In the vascular system with modifiable capacity what finally enters the heart at a diastole is not the same what is initially pushed in the system during systole and depends on dynamic modifications of peripheral vascular bed.

An increase of peripheral vascular compliance is followed by vasodilation and an increase of vascular capacity. Intravascular pressure decreases, blood accumulates in the periphery and less volume comes to the heart. Filling pressure decreases, less blood enters the heart and output of passively filled heart pump goes down proportionally. Lower cardiac output produces less arterial pressure and thereby lower pressure gradient across the vascular circle. Lower pressure gradient causes lower flow rate. Therefore, increase of peripheral vascular compliance and capacity reduces performance of the heart and decrease systemic flow rate independently of the intensity of heart pumping. In the opposite way a decrease of peripheral vascular compliance (vasoconstrictrion) reduces vascular capacity, increases intravascular pressure and returns more blood to the heart. Filling pressure increases with correspondent increase of cardiac output and flow rate. This means that the performance of the heart and systemic flow rate is controlled by the tone of peripheral vessels. The more this peripheral vascular tone the less peripheral intravascular space the more blood returns to the heart and pumped out. Thus, the contraction of smooth muscles of peripheral vessels is active mechanism of control of circulation adjusting systemic flow rate to the sum of current metabolic tissue demands across the body.

That is why the venous return has been introduced in addition to cardiac output to describe cardiovascular function. Venous return is output of the peripheral vascular system that controls performance of the heart what is also typically known as a Starling's law. Conceptually, peripheral vessels contracting and dilating in accordance with local metabolic demands may be considered as an active device controlling circulation that does its work by contracting and expends energy to do mechanical work. Thus, a generally accepted concept of cardiovascular circulation considers peripheral vascular system as major mechanism of controlling systemic flow rate.

Another major mechanism to control systemic flow rate that is also missed by the conventional physiology is modification of circulating volume. Traditional rough mechanistic modeling of the circulation typically considers circulating volume as constant for simplicity. This for a long time prevented the researchers from realizing the powerful effect of changes in circulating volume on the systemic flow rate. Once again, it is a unique feature of the cardiovascular system in combination with other body systems to regulate circulating volume. The major mechanisms of the regulation of circulating volume are active water retention/excretion in the kidney. Water retention increases circulating volume that further distends elastic vascular system with proportional increase of pressure throughout the system including its venous end, i.e., filling pressure. Raising the filling pressure increases filling of the heart and in accordance with Starling's law proportionally increases cardiac output and systemic flow rate. On the contrary, increased water excretion or transcapillary fluid loss leads to reduction of circulating volume with less distension of the vascular walls and lower pressure in the system, filling pressure decreases and cardiac output falls proportionally with reduction of systemic flow rate. Therefore, systemic flow rate may be effectively controlled through active modification of the circulating volume.

All above may be summed up as follows. In accordance with contemporary concept of cardiovascular function basic determinant of effective circulation – systemic flow rate is controlled by peripheral vascular tone and water retention mechanisms but not by the heart pumping activity.

On the contrary, the heart is a passive mechanism of maintaining systemic flow rate adjusted to the summary metabolic demand of the body.

The nature of antigravitational response of the cardiovascular system is predetermined by these unique features: non-sucking type of the heart pump and peripheral control of the circulation. When gravitation shifts blood downward in the upright posture the passively filling heart cannot return blood into the upper body simply by sucking it from the lower body through venous system as it might be the case with artificial pumps. On the contrary, because the heart is positioned in the upper part of the body downward redistribution of blood emptying the upper body causes drop in cardiac filling pressure and, thereby, proportional fall of the output of the passively filling heart. Less blood enters the heart from veins at a diastole and, therefore, is pumped out in arteries in systole. Decrease in cardiac output is followed by decrease of arterial pressure and, thereby, of the pressure gradient across the cardiovascular system. Lower pressure gradient causes lower flow rate across the system and lower return to the heart. The decrease of venous return further decreases cardiac output so that the passively filling heart itself only accelerates and enhances the gravitation-induced downward blood redistribution in upright position pumping blood out of the upper into the lower body until the filling pressure is zero and circulation stops even if the ventricle are still contracting.

Thus, being unable to suck from the veins, the heart itself cannot maintain circulation under gravitational stress. For effective heart pumping in the upright posture the cardiac filling pressure should be increased independently. From the contemporary concept of cardiovascular physiology discussed above there are only two mutually independent but complementary mechanisms to effectively increase filling pressure and maintain pumping function of the non-sucking heart in upright position.

First (and rapid) is vasoconstriction below the heart level, which squeezes blood out of the lower parts of the body and returns it upward against gravitation. Actually, from the analysis presented in the previous chapter there must be a feet-to-head gradient of the degree of vasoconstriction reflecting or mirroring the head-to-feet gradient of the gravitational potential, i.e., power of vasoconstriction should gradually increase from the heart level to the feet. It is amazing but this theoretical conclusion resulted from the current absolutely novel analysis of the effect of gravitation on cardiovascular function has been already proven in clinical studies. Presence of such gradient with maximal vasoconstriction in the legs, less vasoconstriction in the thigh and no vasoconstriction in the neck has been directly demonstrated in the study with centrifugation and Low Body Negative Pressure method (LNBP) [12].

Ideally, this vasoconstrictory mechanism should completely return shifted blood upward and restore the circulation in the upper body. However, gravitation induced head-to-feet blood shift leads to development of extremely high hydrostatic pressure in the lower parts of the body (standing ankle mean arterial pressure rises to about 200 mmHg) that causes transcapillary fluid loss and reduction of the circulating volume – "leakage" of the fluid from the cardiovascular system into the lower-body interstitial spaces. It has been demonstrated in numerous studies that change of the body position from the supine to the standing causes reduction of plasma volume by 180-500 ml during 20 minutes and even greater – 16% during 35-40 minutes. [13]

Accordingly, second (and slow) way to effectively restore cardiac filling pressure is an increase of circulating volume through water retention, which compensate transcapillary fluid loss and independently increases pressure in the vascular system through additional distension of vascular wall with proportional increase of compressing elastic forces. It has been demonstrated that in patients with autonomic failure (PAF and MSA) suffering from orthostatic intolerance ingestion of water prior to standing significantly increase standing blood pressure with improvement in orthostatic symptoms.[14, 15, 16].

As soon as gravitation shifts blood downward in the upright position, the corresponding decrease of arterial pressure in the upper body unloads various baroreceptors (carotid, aortal, coronary, intracardiac etc.) and activates the sympathetic system. All these baroreceptors are located in the upper body and such asymmetric localisation obviously points to their main function as part of mechanism of antigravitational adaptation in upright posture. Activation of sympathetic system causes vasoconstriction and stimulation of the heart. It has been directly shown that compared with the recumbent position, 75° head-up tilt reduced central venous pressure and increased heart rate, MSNA, and plasma epinephrine and norepinephrine levels, suggesting a marked enhancement of overall sympathetic activity [17]. It has also been demonstrated that during exposure to lower body negative pressure that causes similar head-to-feet blood shift in the cardiovascular system the muscle sympathetic nerve activity (MSNA) rose as a function of LBNP ($P < 0.001$, $n = 12$) and interstitial norepinephrine concentrations also increased from 5.2 +/- 0.8 nmol/l at rest to 17.0 +/- 1.7 nmol/l at -50 mmHg ($P < 0.001$).

Low central arterial pressure, low atrial pressure and resulted from decrease of cardiac output low renal arterial pressure are sensed as hypovolemic state and responded by activation of the fluid retention system. Most known part of this water retention system is renin-angiotensin-aldosteron system (RAAS). Activation of water retention mechanisms and in particular RAAS in response to standing is not only well known but even used as diagnostic test that called postural stimulation test and used to detect primary hyperaldosteronism. The test is based on the natural phenomenon of about 50% increase in plasma concentration of aldosterone after 2 hours of upright posture in comparison to supine. In aldosteroma case secretion is constantly high and does not depend on postural changes. The absence of significant increase in aldosteron concentration in upright posture in comparison with horizontal position of the body is indication of the aldosteroma. However, this also clearly means that normally standing causes stimulation of aldosterone production and as a consequence – water retention with increase of circulating volume. There is also a growing body of knowledge regarding humoral mediators such as brain and atrial natriuretic peptides, which directly connects water retention/excretion to the pressure in the upper body circulation.

Vasoconstriction in the lower parts of the body returns blood upward, while water retention increases circulating volume, both contributing to the necessary increase in cardiac filling pressure independently of the heart pumping activity. Once filling pressure is thus restored, the heart is able to respond to sympathetic stimulation with an increase of its output and arterial pressure. The pressure gradient across the system rises and the flow rate proportionally increases to the level necessary to successfully maintain circulation in the upper body and provide sufficient blood supply to the brain. In the study of 10 healthy subjects after 3 days of stable Na and K intake plasma volume fell by 13% (375 +/- 35 ml plasma) over 14 min in standing position, after which time it remained relatively stable. There was a concomitant decrease in systolic blood pressure and an increase in heart rate that peaked at the time of maximal decrease in PV. Plasma epinephrine and norepinephrine increased rapidly to this point. Epinephrine approached baseline by 20 min of standing. norepinephrine spillover increased 80% and clearance decreased 30% with 30 min of standing. The increase in plasma renin activity correlated with an increase in aldosterone. Vasopressin increased progressively, but there was no change in plasma osmolarity. The kidney response showed a significant decrease in Na and an increase in K excretion with upright posture.

This compensatory response providing effective cardiovascular function in upright posture has a price for the cardiovascular system. This price is increased total peripheral vascular resistance due to vasoconstriction requiring, according to Poiseuille's law, a proportional increase in cardiac work and an elevation of arterial pressure. Studies with head-up tilt have demonstrated that the change from the recumbent to the upright position increases peripheral vascular resistance with an increase in arterial pressure, while a return to the recumbency restores it [18, 19]. With gradual tilting, the increases in total peripheral vascular resistance and arterial pressure were found to be proportional to the angle of tilt [20].

The present analysis assumes that gravitation has little effect on horizontally positioned pulmonary circulation, i.e., whatever blood is returned to the right heart is pumped into the pulmonary circulation and returns to the left heart, which pumps it into the systemic circulation.

Chapter 7

CONCEPT OF GRAVITATIONAL STRESS - APPLICATION OF GRAVITATIONAL PHYSICS TO THE HUMAN CARDIOVASCULAR PHYSIOLOGY

When Earth's gravitational field causes downward redistribution of the blood within the cardiovascular system according to gradient of the gravitational potential it does certain work moving blood along the field direction. According to the gravitational physics amount of that work is equal to the product of gradient of gravitational potential and mass of blood shifted by gravitation:

$$W_{shift}=U_{gr}*M_{shift}, \qquad (6)$$

where U_{gr} – gradient of the gravitational potential and M_{shift} -mass of blood shifted by gravitation.

In fact by definition gradient of the gravitational potential U_{gr} is work done by the field in moving unit mass. Then amount of work done in moving a certain mass M_{shift} is the product of the above work of moving unit mass and the value of total mass moved.

In order to restore circulation cardiovascular system must also do the work and move shifted blood back to the upper body. The amount of this work is exactly equal to the amount of work done by the gravitational field in the blood shift. Therefore, gravitational stress may be defined in the following way:

Gravitation causes a significant downward blood shift within the cardiovascular system in the upright position that if not prevented

causes severe circulatory insufficiency with development of deep ischemia of the upper body and the brain.
To maintain adequate circulation in the upper body in such a condition, the cardiovascular system must perform additional work to return blood upward and neutralize the effect of gravitation. The amount of this work, equal to product of the gradient of the gravitational potential and mass of blood shifted, represents the gravitational stress in the cardiovascular system: $gs=w_{up}=u_{gr}{}' m_{shift}$.

The computational aspect of this definition – the formal equation for gravitational stress, however, is not fully practical because gradient of gravitational potential unlike a gradient of electric potential cannot be measured directly. It, however, may be computed indirectly if height of the object is known.

From the mechanics the work performed by any force F in moving an object is product of that force and distance of the movement S:

$$W=F*S, \qquad (7)$$

According to Newton's law of motion force F = ma, where m - mass of the object and a – acceleration of the movement

From the Newton's Universal Law of Gravity gravitational force

$$F_{gr}=G*M*m/r^2 , \qquad (8)$$

where G is the universal gravitational constant: $6.673*10^{-11}\ m^3kg^{-1}s^{-2}$

Therefore we have two equations for the gravitational force F_{gr}. Solving this system of the equations for F_{gr} relatively acceleration of the movement a, we receive

$$F_m=F_{gr},\ ma=G*M*m/r^2,\ a=G*M/r^2 \qquad (9)$$

Traditionally gravitational acceleration is expressed as g instead of a

$$g=G*M/r^2$$

According to this equation gravitation acceleration for interactions between any object and the Earth depends on the mass of the Earth and on the distance r between the center of the Earth and the object.

Thus, we have simplified definition of gravity force

$$F_{gr}=m*g, \qquad (10)$$

where m is mass of the object and g is gravitation acceleration depending on the mass of the Earth and on the distance r.

From this expression acceleration g is a gravitational force that acts on the object with unit mass and has a meaning of the unit gravity force at a distance r between the centers of the interacting objects. In this regard it is an object-independent characteristic or a measure of intensity of the gravitational field created by the object M at a distance r.

When a small object near Earth's surface is moved by the Earth's gravitational field a distance r between centers of the Earth and the object is much more than a distance of the movement S and the absolute value of the r changes insignificantly.

If r1 – the distance between centers of the Earth and the object at the start of the movement, $r2=r1+S$ is the distance between them at the end of the movement and $S<<r1$. Then $r1\approx r2$

This means that g depending on the r also changes insignificantly with such movement.

Therefore, we may take the gravitational acceleration/unit gravity force g as a constant during such movement. Calculation gives value near Earth surface approximately 9.8 ms^{-2}

Now we may express the work done by the Earth's gravitational field in moving unit mass at a distance S as

$$W_u=g*S \tag{11}$$

Direction of the Earth's gravitational field near its surface is vertical so that for the gravitation induced blood shift in the cardiovascular system the distance S is a vertical dimension h - height of the system. Then the work of moving unit mass across the system is

$$W_u=g*h \tag{12}$$

Thus, we received expression for gradient of the gravitational potential through directly measurable parameter h – height of the body (depending on its posture) and constant g. Now the work done by the gravitational field in shifting blood within cardiovascular system is

$$W_{shift}=g*h*M_{shift}, \tag{13}$$

and in such form may be easily calculated.

Chapter 8

GIRAFFE - AN ADEQUATE MODEL OF HUMAN CARDIOVASCULAR SYSTEM

The best illustration of the effect of gravitation on the human cardiovascular system and antigravitational adaptation of the system is giraffe. Being formally quadruped giraffe has an extremely long neck about 10-12 feet (3-3,7 m) in length and half-vertical position of the body so that the cardiovascular system of a giraffe as in bipedal humans most of the time is positioned vertically. According to the above analysis, the cardiovascular system of a giraffe must experience powerful gravitational stress proportional to the extremely high vertical dimension of the system. In order to effectively function under such a great stress the cardiovascular system of giraffe must respond to that stress by performing significant additional workload in preventing blood redistribution to the lower parts of the giraffe's body and keeping blood in his upper part – long neck. Because mechanisms of the antigravitational response are vasoconstriction and increase of circulating volume giraffes must have a high blood pressure and big heart as compared to the animals of the same mass but with predominantly horizontal position of the body. The reality fully corresponds to this conclusion based on application of the theory of gravitation to the concept of cardiovascular physiology. In fact the giraffe's blood pressure is two or three times that of a healthy man, and probably is the highest in the world. The giraffe's heart is huge; it weighs 25 pounds [11 kg], is 2 feet [61 cm] long, and has walls up to 3 inches [7.62 cm] thick. Therefore, the giraffe is strong experimental evidence in support of the above theoretically derived concept of gravitational stress and hypertension as antigravitational adaptation.

Actually, the giraffe, Giraffa Camelopardalis, spending most of the time in upright position provides adequate animal model of human cardiovascular system for investigation of cardiovascular function. Obviously if giraffes and not mice, rats and dogs were used to study human cardiovascular system we would have today completely different concepts of cardiovascular physiology, cardiovascular diseases and possibly treatment practices

Chapter 9

HYPERTENSION AS AN ADVANCED STAGE OF ANTIGRAVITATIONAL RESPONSE

Let us now remember the discovered in space flights studies process of adaptation of human cardiovascular system to gravitational stress after prolonged microgravity. It is easy to note that post-flight adaptation to gravitational stress is very similar to development of essential hypertension. Both processes include increase of sympathetic tone, vasoconstriction, activation of water retention systems, increase of circulating volume, blood pressure and cardiac mass. The almost only difference is the higher range of the similar changes of circulating volume, arterial pressure and cardiac mass occurred in hypertension in comparison with post-microgravity adaptation as if essential hypertension were an advanced stage of the same adaptive process induced by further increase of gravitational stress.

In essence, post flight adaptation is a response of cardiovascular system to the increase of the gravity (measured by unit gravity force or gravitational acceleration) from 0 (weightlessness) to 1G (9.8 at the level of Earth's surface). If the process of this adaptation to the increase of the gravity from 0 to 1G is extrapolated to the higher levels of the gravity above 1G the result will be sympathetic hyperactivity, volume overload, arterial hypertension and cardiac hypertrophy, i.e., typical picture of essential hypertension. .

Hypertensive response to increase in gravitation above 1G has been demonstrated in reality. It has been reported that pilots, who are frequently exposed to +Gz acceleration (a short-term increase in gravitation above 1G), respond to the head-up tilt with a significant increase in arterial pressure compared with non-pilots who had never been exposed to +Gz acceleration [21]. What is more interesting development of chronic arterial hypertension in response to high, sustained +Gz stress induced by centrifugation has been directly demonstrated in rabbits [22].

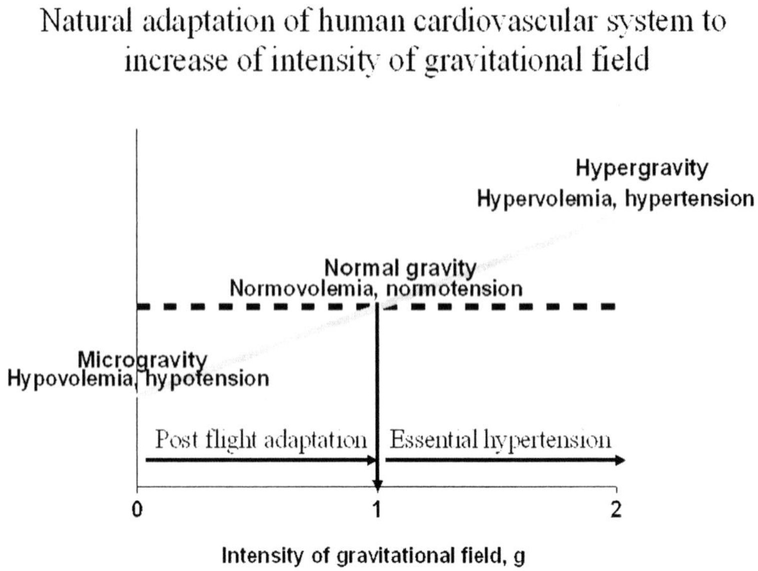

Figure 1. Illustration of the natural course of adaptation of human cardiovascular system to increase of gravity.

However, gravitational stress may be increased without an increase of the gravity force. The nature of he gravitational stress is the downward redistribution of blood in the cardiovascular system. Unlike water in a glass, viscous blood in the complex vascular network redistributes slowly, and the blood shift is not instant, but increases proportionally to the time spent upright. Therefore, in the above equation for gravitational stress, the mass of blood shifted under the influence of gravitation, M_{shift}, is actually a function of time,

$$GS=U_{gr}*M_{shift}(t)=g*h*M_{shift}(t). \qquad (14)$$

In a first approximation this function may be defined, in analogy to electric current from the differential equation $dM_{shift}/dt=U_{gr}/R_d$, where R_d is vascular resistance to gravitation induced downward blood move. This resistance in the arterial part of the cardiovascular system seems to be equal both by physiological meaning and by value to the traditional index of arterial vascular resistance. However, in the venous system gravitation induced downward blood flow is in the most part a backward flow, which is almost completely prevented by venous valves. Thus gravitation induced downward blood flow within cardiovascular system almost exclusively occurs through arterial part and, thereby resistance to that flow is very close by physiological sense and by actual value to arterial resistance or total peripheral vascular resistance . Solution of the above differential equation is linear function of time:

$$M_{shift}(t)=(U_{gr}*t)/R=(g*h*t)/R_d \quad (15)$$

and

$$GS=U_{gr}*M_{shift}(t)=(U_{gr}{}^2*t)/Rd=(g^2*h^2*t)/R_d. \quad (16)$$

This has very important meaning that gravitational stress in the cardiovascular system may be increased not only through increase of the intensity of gravitational field and +Gz acceleration, but also through increase in the time spent upright. In other words excessive stay in upright position imposes abnormally high gravitational stress on the cardiovascular system.

Increase of gravitational stress during excessive stay upright requires advanced stage of antigravitational response with sympathetic hyperactivity, hypervolemia, and arterial hypertension in the same manner as the increase of intensity of gravitational field (unit gravity force) above 1G. Regular (daily) prolonged stay in an upright position should cause chronic systematic increase in the sympathetic activity, circulation volume and arterial pressure, i.e., the development of the typical picture of chronic arterial hypertension. This theoretical conclusion has been proven in a very original way. Rhesus monkeys were experimentally transformed into bipeds using specific fixation of the upper extremities and were forced to walk upright. Forced to spend most of daytime in an upright posture, they developed stable hypertension within 3 months [23].

Thus, great body of theoretical and experimental evidence proves that the most natural cause of chronic arterial hypertension is adaptation to abnormally increased gravitational stress in the cardiovascular system resulting from excessive stay upright.

Chapter 10

NATURAL MECHANISM OF DEFENSE AGAINST GRAVITATIONAL STRESS

No doubt that human cardiovascular system has a built-in mechanism of defense against gravitational stress powerful enough to completely neutralize the gravitation-induced redistribution of blood in the upright posture without additional workload on the cardiovascular system. This mechanism is peripheral pumping.

The lower parts of the body are equipped with a specific blood-pumping device, the calf muscle pump, which is often referred to as the "peripheral venous heart". Deep veins of the calf going within fascial muscle compartments have valves, which, like the heart valves, prevent backward blood flow and are able to endure pressures of several hundred of mm Hg. Squeezing the vein segment during muscle contraction causes valves to close and blood to flow upward in the deep vein segment above. With regular contractions of the calf muscles in upright position, blood is pumped out of the lower parts of the body against gravitation, neutralizing gravitation-induced downward blood shift.

Therefore, inability of the heart to suck blood from venous side of the cardiovascular circuit is effectively compensated by the presence of the additional pump in the venous system. These two non-sucking pumps together form an effective pumping device which does not depend on filling pressure and successfully maintains circulation in an upright posture.

Thus finally the equation of gravitational stress takes the following form:

$$GS=(g^2{}'h^2{}'t)/R_d-W_{per}, \qquad (17)$$

where W_{per} is the work of the calf muscle pump.

This mechanism, however, is only active during regular calf contractions, i.e., walking. From this analysis walking is natural condition for the human during upright posture.

Chapter 11

Prolonged Sitting - The Best Way to Increase Gravitational Stress in the Cardiovascular System

Upright posture has two basic forms sitting and standing. Of these two sitting seems to be specifically designed to increase gravitational stress in the cardiovascular system:

1. First, modern sitting is not sitting on the ground, but rather on a chair, i.e., in an upright posture with significant height and thereby a high vertical gradient of the gravitational potential.
2. Second, sitting is much more comfortable than standing and, therefore, allows significantly longer duration of stay.
3. Third and most important, sitting, in contrast to standing, almost completely inactivates the natural defensive mechanism of calf muscle pumping.

Even though standing allows development of a larger gravitational potential gradient, it rarely lasts as long as sitting and is usually accompanied by involuntary calf movement, i.e., activity of the peripheral pumps decreasing gravitational stress.

Thus, prolonged sitting (e.g. office work, driving, and so on) causes a powerful increase of gravitational stress in the cardiovascular system and, thereby, have to be responded by advanced stages of the antigravitational response with sympathetic hyperactivity, powerful vasoconstriction, volume overloading and hypertension.

These effects of prolonged sitting have been directly demonstrated in some clinical studies. It has been reported that sitting for 5 h (1st vs. 5th h) resulted in an increase in calf venous pooling (17%) and increases in diastolic and mean arterial pressures (6 and 7.3 mmHg, respectively) [24, 25]. Prevalence of hypertension was found to be significantly higher among workers with a typical sitting posture at work, e.g. drivers and air traffic controllers, than among employed individuals in general [26, 27].

Chapter 12

ESSENTIAL HYPERTENSION AS AN ADAPTATION OF THE CARDIOVASCULAR SYSTEM TO THE "SITTING" LIFESTYLE

Now taking into account described above natural defensive mechanism of peripheral pumping and analysis of sitting posture total period spent upright must be divide from the concept of gravitational stress into two principally different states: standing or sitting when gravitational stress in the cardiovascular system increases and walking or other upright activities with regular calf contractions like running, bicycling and so on when gravitational stress in the cardiovascular system decreases and even may be completely eliminated. Real level of daily gravitational stress depends on the actual proportion of both types of upright condition and, of course the time spent supine. The greater proportion of inactive upright posture the higher gravitational stress in the cardiovascular system. As it was mentioned above except a few specific cases of military or professional service time spent standing usually is much shorter than time spent sitting and may be neglected. Thus, it is sitting time that really determines level of daily gravitational stress experienced by the cardiovascular system.

During second half of XXth century focus of business has shifted from manufacturing to service. This had a significant impact on a lifestyle. Various types of physical labor was replaced with typical for sphere of service office work. Office work is almost totally made while sitting so that the daily portion of time spent in sitting posture is increased by several times for office workers resulting in development of abnormally high gravitational stress.

Another factor causing profound changes in the work style is rapid progress of information technologies and computerization of manufacturing processes in such a way that most of technical operations are performed automatically while humans in the industry work exclusively as video display terminal (VDT) operators, i.e., again spend their work hours sitting.

Add here universal use of cars, trains, buses and other transportation machines that extends sitting time and reduces walking; also daily time of sitting before TV set and the result is lifestyle with prolonged sitting during both work and leisure times – "sitting" lifestyle.

From the above analysis of the effect of gravitation on the human cardiovascular system "sitting" lifestyle is a way to systematically and powerfully increase gravitational stress in the cardiovascular system that requires development of chronic advanced antigravitational adaptation in the form of sympathetic hyperactivity, volume overloading and arterial hypertension. In other words, "sitting" lifestyle unavoidably causes development of typical picture of essential hypertension – chronic hypertension that is not caused by any other disease or pathological condition. Actually, essential hypertension itself may be considered as manifestation of increased gravitational stress in the cardiovascular system associated with sitting lifestyle.

This powerful stress manifested by high blood pressure causes progressive damage of the cardiovascular system and is a major cause of global epidemy of cardiovascular disease in modern world.

Chapter 13

NATURAL COURSE OF ESSENTIAL HYPERTENSION OR DEVELOPMENT OF STRUCTURAL ADAPTATION TO EXCESSIVE GRAVITATIONAL STRESS

At first the above described adaptive changes in the cardiovascular system in response to increased gravitational stress are mostly functional and, therefore, reversible. In horizontal position blood returns from the lower to the upper parts of the body and both the sympathetic and water retention system are deactivated. Vascular tone decreases and peripheral vascular resistance returns to normal, though circulating volume remains increased because of slower dynamics of the volume changes. Arterial pressure is elevated during daytime upright posture only and returns to normal during horizontal nighttime rest. At this stage, change from upright to horizontal position is followed by a feet-to-head shift of increased circulating volume to the central part of the cardiovascular system located in the upper body with a transient increase in filling pressure and cardiac output. Due to this effect, a typical study of cardiac function (echocardiography or any other) performed on a patient after several minutes in the horizontal position detects increased cardiac output and normal peripheral resistance. Thus, the first "hyperkinetic" phase of hypertension is diagnosed. If such study were performed in upright position of the body it would detect normal cardiac output and increased peripheral resistance. If such study were performed after significant time in the supine posture it would also detect normal cardiac output and normal peripheral resistance. Once again the effect of gravitation on circulating blood is completely ignored . It is interesting that this effect of postural changes on cardiac function has been documented in studies with low-degree head-down tilt (close to supine position with only 5-6 degree of tilt). A study of 20-hr bed rest with head-down tilt (-5 degrees) showed that central venous pressure increased from 8.6 to 12.6 cm H_2O, cardiac output - from 6.9 to 7.9 liters/min, and stroke volume - from 104 to 113 ml after 15 minutes of tilt, but all values returned to baseline within 20 hours [28]. In controlled study with head-down tilt (-6 degrees), stroke volume increased from 65 to 88 ml and cardiac output increased from 4.6 to 5.4 l/min ($P<0.05$) during 15 min of tilt ($P<0.05$) with no change during that time in seated controls [29]). These data demonstrate amazing inadequacy of current approach to evaluation of human cardiovascular function. Yet this approach is used as basis for development of interventions. Therefore, it is not surprising that contemporary cardiovascular medicine failed to prevent growth of morbidity and mortality from cardiovascular disease.

In the course of time, energy-consuming vasoconstriction is replaced by structural changes of the vascular walls: vascular remodeling with a persistent decrease in compliance and capacitance and correspondent increase in elastic resistance. The structurally dependent increase in vascular resistance remains in horizontal position so that cardiac work and arterial pressure are now constantly increased causing left ventricular hypertrophy. The process of structural adaptation in the lower parts of the body involves microcirculation and results in decrease of capillary permeability. With decreased permeability there is less transcapillary fluid loss and reduction of circulating volume in upright posture. The persistent decrease in vascular compliance increases the pressure-volume relationship (shifts pressure-volume curve to the left) in the cardiovascular system so that less circulating volume is necessary to maintain sufficient filling pressure. The water-retention system is deactivated and circulating volume decreases. Finally with reduced blood volume and rigid vascular walls there is no central blood shift in the cardiovascular system during posture change from upright to supine and, therefore, no transient increase in cardiac output, while total peripheral resistance is permanently increased. At this stage, a typical study of cardiac function in the horizontal position detects the "normokynetic" phase of hypertension (normal cardiac output and increased peripheral resistance).

Blood flow in arterial system is pulsing. With each contraction stroke volume is thrown into arterial system and hits the vascular walls. When heart contracts the arterial system experience a hydrodynamical stroke that causes sharp increase of mechanical pressure on the vascular walls – circumferential stress with correspondent increase of transmural pressure. Increase of blood pressure in the course of hypertension causes correspondent increase of power of hydrodynamical strokes experienced by vascular wall during systole. With lower compliance and higher blood pressure there is also increase in shear stress – friction between blood flow and vascular wall. Both processes causes mechanical traumatization of vascular walls. Major mechanical trauma - breakup of vessel causes hemorrhage while minor traumas results in atherosclerotic scars of the vessels. These atherosclerotic lesions progress and accumulate with progression of hypertension eventually leading to severe obstruction of arteries. Also substantial atherosclerotic changes of the inner surface of the vessels predispose to massive thrombosis with complete occlusion of arterial lumen. Therefore, substantial increase in power of hydrodynamical stress on the vascular walls in the course of hypertension causes progressive damage of the cardiovascular system resulting in development of the life-threatening complications: brain stroke, myocardial infarction and sudden death that accounts for major part of death and disability in the industrial world.

Chapter 14

GRAVITATION AS A REASON FOR SEASONAL VARIATIONS OF BLOOD PRESSURE LEVEL

The effect of gravitation on the human cardiovascular system may explain many phenomena that remains unanswered by conventional concepts. One of such phenomena is seasonal variations in blood pressure level with higher values in winter than in summer. This phenomenon may be easily explained by gravitational effect. However, in this case it is not Earth's but sun gravitation involved.

Earth's axis is tilted some 23.5 degrees against the Earth-Sun plane. This means that during significant periods of the year (winter and summer) Earth surface on the poles and surrounding area are either tilt away or tilt to the Sun. Due to this effect of Earth axis being not perpendicular to the plane of its orbit people in the parts of the globe outside of tropical zone has Sun below the the horizon for most part of the 24-h period in winter and above the horizon – in summer. Consequently Sun gravitation is applied to human body mostly in head-to-feet direction during winter and in feet-to-head direction during summer. Therefore, gravitational stress on the cardiovascular system of people outside of tropical zone is additionally increased during winter (Earth gravitation plus Sun gravitation) and decreased during summer(Earth gravitation minus Sun gravitation) with proportional seasonal variation in power of antigravitational response including blood pressure level.

Chapter 15

INHERITANCE OF HYPERTENSION

In most part what is typically considered as disease inheritance actually means a family history of the disease. Inheritance in strict sense is a transmission of specific genes (alleles) from parents to children. Such transmission of genotype may be manifested by inheritance of correspondent phenotype - disease and accounts for family history of it. However, family history of a disease is more general phenomenon meaning that a part or all members of the same family have that disease and may be caused not only by the same genotype but also some other factors. For example, children may live in the same environment as parents and be exposed to the same environmental factors. Another possible cause is inheritance of lifestyle habits. The children may copy the parent's pattern of eating or physical activity or have the same profession. Therefore, family history of a disease does not necessarily mean that it has genetic origin.

In essence, the concept of hypertension as adaptation to increased gravitational stress associated with modern sitting life style considers this lifestyle as a primary cause of the disease and transmission of lifestyle pattern from parents to children may fully explain family history of hypertension.

However, genetic transmission still may play some role in that phenomenon. For example, some conditions contributing to additional increase of gravitational stress or capable to affect antigravitational response of the cardiovascular system may be genetically transmitted and partially account for family history of hypertension.

According to the above equation expressing general model of the gravitational stress in human cardiovascular system it depends on the mass of blood shifted by gravitation. Though it is not obvious from the equation but this mass should be directly proportional to the total mass of circulating blood. Thus, the equation for the amount of mass shifted by the gravitation in fact is

$$M_{shift}=k_m*M_t*U_{gr}*t,$$

where M_t – total mass of circulating blood and k_m – coefficient that is mass portion of total circulating blood shifted per unit time.

Total mass of blood is obviously proportional to the body mass. Then overweighting should cause additional increase of the gravitational stress and blood pressure through this mechanism of increasing of mass of blood shifted by gravitation in upright posture. The more mass of the body the more total mass of blood and the more absolute mass of blood shifted by gravitation Therefore, in the overweighted body more blood is shifted by gravitation and more heavy weight should be lifted up by cardiovascular system to maintain upper body circulation. Body constitution and, therefore, weight in significant part is genetically determined and thereby genetically inherited. Then inheritance of hypertension may indirectly depend on inheritance of body constitution.

The gravitational potential in upright posture is also directly proportional to the height of the system and thereby of the body. The tall people should experience greater gravitational stress than short. Therefore, excessive height is factor contributing to development of hypertension. Then genetic transmission of tall constitution may contribute to family history of hypertension.

Another condition that may play important role in this regard is venous disorders. In fact resistance to downward move of blood under influence of gravitation in upright posture depends on how effectively venous valves prevents that move. If their work is not good then more blood will be shifted in upright posture and, therefore, more work is necessary to lift it up into the upper body. Therefore, venous disease may contribute to development of essential hypertension as antigravitational response. In practice arterial hypertension is frequently associated with venous disease. The gravitational hypothesis of hypertension as a response to increased gravitational stress easily explains this frequent association of essential hypertension with venous disease as two related consequences of the weakness of venous walls and incompetence of venous valves leading to significant increase of gravitation induced blood shift in cardiovascular system and excessive pooling of blood in venous system of the legs. There is a generally accepted concept of venous disease as connective tissue disorder leading to weakness of venous walls and underdevelopment and incompetence of venous valves. Then transmission of gene responsible for correspondent collagenopathy may indirectly contribute to the family history of hypertension

Thus, family history may be easily explained by the inheritance of lifestyle habits and professions even without genetic mechanisms. However, it may also have indirect genetic component.

Chapter 16

MEANING OF SYSTOLIC AND DIASTOLIC ARTERIAL PRESSURE FROM THE STANDPOINT OF ESSENTIAL HYPERTENSION AS ADVANCED COMPENSATORY RESPONSE TO INCREASED GRAVITATIONAL STRESS, EXPLANATION OF AGE DEPENDENT DECREASE OF DIASTOLIC PRESSURE

From the standpoint of the concept of essential hypertension as adaptation to excessive gravitational stress, the traditional indices of diastolic and systolic pressures receive a different meaning. As it was mentioned above primary source of pressure in the cardiovascular system is elastic resistance of distended vascular system. Heart only redistributes this background pressure between arterial and venous parts of the system creating pressure gradient across the system. If there is no vascular resistance, e.g. no blood and, thereby, no distension in the system or extremely high vascular compliance, the pressure is zero. Elastic resistance of closed vascular system creates pressure is a function of vascular compliance and circulating volume. Under the influence of gravitation there is a third argument of this function independent of vascular compliance and blood volume t. It is gradient of the gravitational potential across the system. This gradient redistributes pressure created by vascular resistance in head-to-feet direction so that correspondent hydrostatic pressure gradient is created. This hydrostatic pressure (resulted from vascular resistance and gravitation) determines background level of pressure in the cardiovascular system gradually increasing from head where it is minimal to feet where it is maximal. This hydrostatic pressure does not depend on phases of cardiac cycle and remains constant during it. To provide blood flow in the lowest parts of the body the heart must develop a pressure higher then hydrostatic pressure in those parts in order to create a pressure gradient as moving force for blood flow. This means that vertical hydrostatic pressure gradient determines the lowest possible level of aortal pressure during cardiac cycle, i.e., diastolic pressure.

Thus, diastolic arterial pressure reflects hydrostatic pressure gradient in the vascular (arterial) system that is directly proportional to the gradient of the gravitational potential and circulating volume. In other words diastolic blood pressure is an index of actual gravitation-induced downward blood shift within the cardiovascular system.

When heart is pumping it injects stroke volume in the vascular system during systole and receive some volume back in diastole. These rapid changes of volume through the vascular system causes correspondent changes of pressure. Because the elastic forces of the vascular walls are proportional to the level of distension this pressure component strictly depends on the phase of cardiac cycle being greatest in the mid-systole when distension is maximal while disappearing at the end of diastole when distension is minimal.

Thus, systolic arterial pressure is diastolic arterial pressure plus pressure increase due to additional distension of vascular (arterial) system by stroke volume during heart contraction. This pressure increase is a function of vascular (arterial) compliance and stroke volume, which in turn strictly depends on venous return (Starling's law). Therefore, systolic pressure is an index of compensatory vasoconstriction or vascular remodelling that is major factor of increase of cardiac work.

Summarizing all above we may say that increase in diastolic arterial pressure indicates an increase in hydrostatic pressure gradient resulted from the downward blood shift within the cardiovascular system and/or increase of circulating volume, i.e., gravitational stress in the system, while the increase in systolic pressure indicates an active compensatory response of the cardiovascular system to that stress. This gives quite different meanings to the traditional indices of systolic and diastolic pressure in regard to evaluation of essential hypertension.

According to the above analysis an increase in diastolic pressure alone does not indicate increased work of the cardiovascular system unless it is accompanied by an increase in systolic pressure. This means that diastolic pressure alone does not really indicate severity of pathologic process of essential hypertension (however, it still may do that in regard to the secondary hypertension).

In clinical practice doctors are often see a kind of hypertension with dominating elevation of diastolic pressure and a very mild increase of systolic pressure (with remarkably low pulse pressure). The patients usually share the following common characteristics: young and middle age, more often women, low physical tolerance, subtle edema of feet in the evening and face in the morning, low heat tolerance, othostatic hypotensive reactions, frequent headache and dizziness.

Typically, this kind of hypertension is a result of mild impairment of vasoconstriction so that excessive gravitational blood shift is compensated mostly by water retention. Edema of legs and feet in the evening and of face in the morning are the redistribution of excessive water volume. During daytime upright posture the excessive liquid accumulates in the legs and feet while during night it redistributes throughout the whole body including head and face .

Water retention is slow mechanism that is not able to rapidly respond to physical activity and correspondent increase of tissue demands in blood supply. During physical exercise increase of sympathetic activity does not causes correspondent vasoconstriction and increase of venous return to the heart. The only result is rapid increase of heart rate without significant increase of cardiac output and inability to increase physical activity any further.

Heat causes subcutaneous venodilation and decrease of venous return to the heart followed by respective fall in cardiac output. Compensatory sympathexcitation causes ineffective tachycardia and does not prevent reduction of blood supply to the brain with development of headache, dizziness and in severe cases syncope.

On the other side the weak vasoconstriction does not cause significant increase of total peripheral vascular resistance and, thereby, systolic pressure and cardiac work. Less mechanical stress in the cardiovascular system leads to less damage of the system in the long run.

Therefore, increase in diastolic pressure without correspondent increase in systolic pressure means that there is abnormally high gravitational stress in upright posture, which compensated mostly through increase of circulating volume without significant increase of vascular resistance and thereby work of the cardiovascular system. Such condition though limits physical capacity of a person is beneficial from long term perspective because it is less harmful for cardiovascular system.

On the contrary, elevation of systolic pressure directly points to the increase of vascular resistance and thereby to growing mechanical stress in the cardiovascular system. High mechanical stress in the cardiovascular system causes its more rapid and severe damages.

Thus, from the standpoint of the concept of essential hypertension as advanced antigravitational response increase of systolic and diastolic arterial pressures have different meanings. In short increase of systolic and diastolic pressures reflects relative activity of two mechanisms of compensation of the gravitation-induced downward blood shift in upright posture. Systolic pressure elevation is index of activity of vasoconstrictory mechanism associated with significant increase of mechanical stress in the cardiovascular system and rapid damage of the system. Diastolic blood pressure elevation is index of activity of water retention mechanism of compensation, which does not significantly increase mechanical stress in the cardiovascular system and, therefore, does not damage the system but also is insufficient during intense physical activity and exposure to heat.

Chapter 17

ETIOLOGICAL TREATMENT AND PREVENTION OF ESSENTIAL HYPERTENSION AS A CONSEQUENCE OF EXCESSIVE GRAVITATIONAL STRESS

Concept of essential hypertension as advanced antigravitational response to excessive sitting unique in the sense that it first time in history offers ethological treatment and prevention of the disease. According to the given concept ethiological treatment of essential hypertension is elimination of excessive gravitational stress in the cardiovascular system. In this regard preventive and treatment measures naturally fall in the two major categories: measures to reduce gravitational stress and measures to activate natural defense mechanisms.

From the developed equation of gravitational stress in the cardiovascular system (17) the magnitude of the stress may be reduced in the following ways:

1. decrease of gradient of the gravitational potential across the system during sitting
2. decrease of sitting time
3. lowering weight

According to the theory of gravitational physics gradient of the gravitational potential across cardiovascular system depends on height of the system. Height of the sitting posture may be decreased through reclining of the body and/or leg elevation, as in a dentist's chair (remember also the comfort of resting the feet on a table). Fortunately, there is a plenty of so-called zero gravity chairs available from numerous manufacturers that reduces vertical dimension of the body during sitting to negligible level from the standpoint of gravitational stress in the cardiovascular system. Also those chairs provide comfortable environment to the seater. Some of them allow to change the position (angle) automatically just by pushing a button. Thus, using these zero gravity chairs is method of etiological treatment of essential hypertension.

Second, time spent upright may be reduced by changing sitting into lying or walking whenever it is possible (it is worth noting that in antique times people even ate lying). Practically this method may be realized in the form of short time breaks spent supine or walking (e.g. using treadmill) .

The last and not obvious way has been explained above in the discussion of the mechanisms of inheritance of essential hypertension as advanced antigravitational response. When blood moves downward in the cardiovascular system the amount of blood that is displaced in any certain period of time is proportional to the total mass of blood. Obviously, the more the total mass of blood the more blood is displaced by gravitation. Therefore, lowering weight of the body reduces total mass of circulating blood and, thereby, mass of blood shifted by gravitation. This eventually decrease gravitational stress in the cardiovascular system. Therefore, weight reduction is not just a non-drug measure of blood pressure reduction but effective etiological treatment of essential hypertension.

Alternatively, abnormally high gravitational stress in the cardiovascular system may be eliminated through activation of mechanism of natural defense. This activation is possible generally in two ways:

1. Natural - daily regular walking or exercise with regular calf contractions.
2. Artificial - performing foot exercises with walking-type foot flexions while sitting at work

Active calf muscle pumping provides a much more rapid and powerful blood shift into the upper body than the initial passive downward redistribution induced by gravitation. Even very short period of calf exercise may completely restore passive blood shift resulting from hours of sitting and eliminate excessive gravitational stress in the cardiovascular system. When blood shift is restored during calf exercises mechanism of antigravitational response is deactivated. Regular complete deactivation of antigravitational adaptive mechanism prevents its progression to the phase of structural adaptation and stabilization of hypertension.

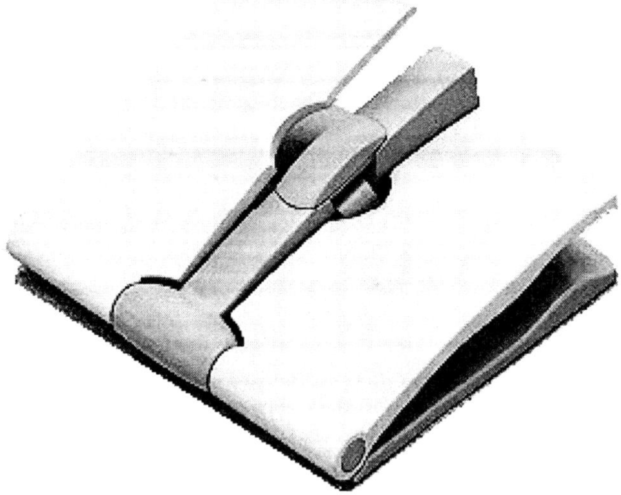

Figure 2. The Lightfeet Exercise Machine from **Dr. GREEN Natural Products** is an example of marketed devices for feet exercise performed while sitting aimed at normalization of limbs circulation. Use of such devices may be offered as ethiological treatment of essential hypertension from the standpoint of gravitational theory of its origin.

It has been demonstrated in a large long-term study that 20 minutes or more of walking even once a week significantly reduces the risk of developing hypertension among normotensive men [30]. Walking 10,000 steps/day or more has been reported to reduce blood pressure and sympathetic nerve activity in mild essential hypertension [31]. Up to date there is already some common, however, incomplete understanding of the relationships between physical activity/exercise and development of hypertension. On the basis of the above and similar data from clinical studies a general conclusion has been made that low physical activity is a factor contributing to the development of hypertension and cardiovascular disease and also that regular physical exercise prevents development of both of them. Being close to the developed concept of gravitational stress this general idea neither explains mechanisms of how low physical activity contributes to the development of hypertension and other cardiovascular diseases nor it differentiates between the kinds of physical activity and considers any physical activity as preventive in this regard. According to the developed concept of essential hypertension as advanced antigravitational adaptation it is not just low physical activity that causes the disease but exactly - prolonged sitting doing so through increase of gravitational stress in the cardiovascular system. If this concept is true then only physical activity with regular calf contractions is effective as measure to reduce blood pressure while others kinds of exercises are not. It is amazing, but this has already been demonstrated in clinical study - that only exercise with regular calf muscle activity leads to a decrease in blood pressure, while other types of exercise may even increase it [32]. This result specifically proves the suggested mechanism of arterial hypertension as a compensatory response to gravitation-induced downward blood shift within the cardiovascular system in the upright position. Thus, on the basis of theoretical analysis and results of clinical studies walking from 20 minutes to one hour (approximate time necessary to make 10,000 steps) may be recommended as an effective treatment of hypertension.

Artificial activation of peripheral calf muscle pump during sitting is possible through performing walking-like foot flexions with regular contractions of the calves. This may be done simply as an easy physical exercise not requiring significant efforts or concentration. Today there is also a plenty of available commercial devices, which are specifically designed to help perform regular foot flexions while sitting. Basically such devices have been developed as a preventive measure against venous disease and thromboembolism. Now these devices, however, may receive the new indication of etiological treatment/prevention of essential hypertension through prevention of increase of gravitational stress in the cardiovascular system during prolonged sitting.

Chapter 18

INTEGRATING EXISTING CONCEPTS

This concept of excessive gravitational stress as primary cause of essential hypertension is not just another hypothesis alternatively explaining the disease development. In essence, this gravitational hypothesis of essential hypertension fully integrates the two other major concepts of origin of the disease: primary increase of sodium reabsorption and primary sympathetic hyperactivity as two complementary mechanisms of adaptation to gravitational stress. In fact both aforementioned hypotheses are not logically complete because neither primary increase of sodium reabsorption nor primary increase of sympathetic activity is explained. Obviously there must be a cause for either abnormality. It has been suggested that mutations of certain genes are responsible for specific enzymopathies underlying primary sympathetic hyperactivity as well as primary increase of sodium reabsorption. However, these suggestions have never been proven in humans. Theory of gravitational stress in human cardiovascular system easily explains both phenomena as natural countermeasures against downward blood shift induced by gravitation aimed at maintaining filling of non-sucking heart and circulation of the upper body.

Therefore, all theoretical developments and experimental evidence under each of those concepts automatically become natural parts of the gravitational hypothesis of essential hypertension. In this regard the gravitational hypothesis is perfect harmonization of existed knowledge.

Using mathematical terminology this concept is natural expansion of Guyton's idea of hypertension. Arthur Guyton after years of experimental studies of cardiovascular system has finally come to idea of autoregulation of blood pressure that he called a principle of «infinite gain»: increase of sympathetic tone leads to increase of blood pressure that causes proportional increase of filtration in kidneys and, thereby, decrease of circulating volume. Reduction of circulating volume returns blood pressure level to previous state despite increased sympathetic activity. Decrease of sympathetic tone reduces vascular resistance and, thereby, blood pressure. Then filtration is reduced proportionally and circulating volume increases restoring blood pressure. The only possibility for blood pressure to rise in such system is kidney resetting to the greater circulating volume. Following this logic he suggested that there must be a primary defect in kidney causing water retention and stable increase of higher circulating volume. Due to nature of mechanisms of water metabolism the most appropriate candidate for that role is increase of sodium reabsorption causing proportional water retention and as a consequence increase of circulating volume. Yet he could not find the reason why kidneys should reset in this way. Obviously that was because he always made his preparations for experimental study of cardiovascular function in horizontal plane and that imprinted horizontal view of cardiovascular system in his mind. Should he ever see or imagine the system in vertical position he will immediately discover that reason.

Despite full harmony with existed concepts of hypertension this gravitational hypothesis completely reverses the perspective of treatment of the disease because it considers essential hypertension as a result of adoption of the adverse life-style and offers a way to complete healing and prevention of the disease through the elimination of the primary factor of excessive gravitational stress. Variety of established factors contributing to the development of essential hypertension, including inherited anomalies, such as polymorphisms and mutations in the genes of angiotensinogen, angiotensin-converting enzyme, b2-adrenergic receptor, adducin, angiotensinase C, renin-binding protein, protein b3-subunit, atrial natriuretic factor, and the insulin receptor, as well as hypertensiogenic factors, such as obesity, high alcohol intake, high salt intake, stress, dyslipidemia, low potassium or calcium intake, are not rejected under this hypothesis, but considered as secondary, i.e., unable to cause hypertension without the primary factor of regular, prolonged remaining in an upright posture.

This hypothesis of essential hypertension as response of the cardiovascular system to “sitting” lifestyle is scientifically sound perspective of complete victory over the hypertension and possibly over the whole epidemy of the cardiovascular disease. It gives hope to billions and needs further development and testing. Now it is simply a seed sown. in hope that the readers of this book will find it interesting and help it grow until it brings its fruit.

REFERENCES

[1] American Heart Association. Heart Disease and Stroke Statistics–2005 Update. Available at *http://www.americanheart.org/statistics*. Last accessed January 12, 2005.

[2] Kearney PM, Whelton M, Reynolds K, Muntner P, Whelton PK, He J. Global burden of hypertension: analysis of worldwide data. *Lancet.* 2005 Jan 15;365(9455):217-23.

[3] Chalmers J et al. WHO-ISH Hypertension Guidelines Committee. 1999 World Health Organization - International Society of Hypertension Guidelines for the Management of Hypertension. *J Hypertens*, 1999, 17:151-185.

[4] Turnbull F; Blood Pressure Lowering Treatment Trialists' Collaboration. Effects of different blood-pressure-lowering regimens on major cardiovascular events: results of prospectively-designed overviews of randomised trials. *Lancet.* 2003 Nov 8; 362(9395): 1527-35.

[5] JM Fritsch-Yelle, JB. Charles, MM. Jones, and ML. Wood. Microgravity decreases heart rate and arterial pressure in humans. *J. AppZ. PhysioZ.* 80(3): 910-914,1996.

[6] M. A. Perhonen, F. Franco, L. D. Lane, J. C. Buckey, C. G. Blomqvist, J. E. Zerwekh, R. M. Peshock, P. T. Weatherall, and B. D. Levine Cardiac atrophy after bed rest and spaceflight. *J Appl Physiol*, August 1, 2001; 91(2): 645 - 653.

[7] Arbeille P, Fomina G, Roumy J, Alferova I, Tobal N, Herault S. Adaptation of the left heart, cerebral and femoral arteries, and jugular and femoral veins during short- and long-term head-down tilt and spaceflights. *Eur J Appl Physiol* 2001 Dec;86(2):157-68.

[8] Fritsch-Yelle, J. M., J. B. Charles, M. M. Jones, L. A. Beightol, and D. L. Eckberg. Spaceflight alters autonomic regulation of arterial pressure in humans. *J. Appl. Physiol.* 77:1776-1783,1994.

[9] Whitson, P. A., J. B. Charles, and W. J. Williams. Changes in sympathoadrenal response to standing in humans after space flight. *J. AppZ. Physiol.* 79: 428-433, 1995.

[10] Levine BD, Pawelczyk JA, Ertl AC, Cox JF, Zuckerman JH, Diedrich A, Biaggioni I, Ray CA, Smith ML, Iwase S, Saito M, Sugiyama Y, Mano T, Zhang R, Iwasaki K, Lane LD, Buckey JC Jr, Cooke WH, Baisch FJ, Eckberg DL, Blomqvist CG. Human muscle sympathetic neural and haemodynamic responses to tilt following spaceflight. *J Physiol.* 2002 Jan 1;538(Pt 1):331-40.

[11] Buckey JC Jr, Lane LD, Levine BD, Watenpaugh DE, Wright SJ, Moore WE, Gaffney FA, Blomqvist CG. Orthostatic intolerance after spaceflight. *J Appl Physiol.* 1996 Jul;81(1):7-18.

[12] Donald E. Watenpaugh, Gregory A. Breit, Theresa M. Buckley, Richard E. Ballard, Gita Murthy, and Alan R. Hargens. Human cutaneous vascular responses to whole-body tilting, Gz centrifugation, and LBNP. *J Appl Physiol* 96: 2153-2160, 2004.

[13] HAGAN, R. D., F. J. DIAZ, AND S. M. HORVATH.PL. Volume changes with movement to supine and standing positions. *J. Appl. Physiol.: Respirat. Environ. Exercise Physiol.* 45(3): 414-418, 1978.

[14] Young TM, Mathias CJ. The effects of water ingestion on orthostatic hypotension in two groups of chronic autonomic failure: multiple system atrophy and pure autonomic failure. *J Neurol Neurosurg Psychiatry*. 2004 Dec;75(12):1737-41.

[15] Cariga P, Mathias CJ. Haemodynamics of the pressor effect of oral water in human sympathetic denervation due to autonomic failure. *Clin Sci* (Lond). 2001 Sep;101(3):313-9.

[16] Jordan J, Shannon JR, Black BK, Ali Y, Farley M, Costa F, Diedrich A, Robertson RM, Biaggioni I, Robertson D. The pressor response to water drinking in humans : a sympathetic reflex? *Circulation.* 2000 Feb 8;101(5):504-9.

[17] Furlan et al. Neural Sympathetic Oscillations During Tilt. *Circulation.* 2000;101:886-892.

[18] Vargas E, Lye M, Faragher EB, Goddard C, Moser B, Davies I. Cardiovascular haemodynamics and the response of vasopressin, aldosterone, plasma renin activity and plasma catecholamines to head-up tilt in young and old healthy subjects. *Age Ageing 1986* Jan;15(1):17-28.

[19] Delis KT, Nicolaides AN, Stansby G. Effect of posture on popliteal artery hemodynamics. *Arch Surg* 2000 Mar;135(3):265-9.

[20] Hainsworth R, Al-Shamma YMH. Cardiovascular responses to upright tilting in healthy subjects. *Clin Sci* 1988; 74:17–22.

[21] Newman DG, White SW, Callister R. Evidence of baroreflex adaptation to repetitive +Gz in fighter pilots. *Aviat Space Environ Med* 1998 May;69(5):446-51.

[22] Borredon P, Paillard F, Liscia P, Nogues C.Hypertension induced by repeated exposure to high sustained +Gz (HS +Gz). *Aviat Space Environ Med* 1985 Apr;56(4):328-32.

[23] Belkaniia GS, Dartsmeliia VA [Upright walking as a factor in the development of arterial hypertension inprimates] *Kosm Biol Aviakosm Med.* 1984 May-Jun;18(3):14-9.

[24] Belkaniia GS, Dartsmeliia VA [Upright walking as a factor in the development of arterial hypertension inprimates] *Kosm Biol Aviakosm Med.* 1984 May-Jun;18(3):14-9.

[25] Shvartz E, Gaume JG, Reibold RC, Glassford EJ, White RT. Effect of the circutone seat on hemodynamic, subjective, and thermal responses to prolonged sitting. *Aviat Space Environ Med* 1982 Aug;53(8):795-802.

[26] D.R. Ragland, M.A. Winkleby, J. Schwalbe, B. Holman, L. Morse, L. Syme and J.M. Fisher: Prevalence of hypertension in bus drivers, in *International Journal of Epidemiology*, Vol. 16, No. 2, 1987, pp. 208-214

[27] S. Cobb and R.M. Rose. Hypertension, peptic ulcer and diabetes in air traffic controllers. *Journal of the American Medical Association*, No. 224, 1973, pp. 489-492.

[28] Gaffney FA, Nixon JV, Karlsson ES et al: Cardiovascular deconditioning produced by 20 hours of bed rest with head-down tilt (-5 degrees) in middle-aged healthy men. *Am J Cardiol*, 1985; 56(10): 634–38.

[29] Shiraishi M, Schou M, Gybel M et al: Comparison of acute cardiovascular responses to water immersion and head-down tilt in humans. *J Appl Physiol*, 2002; 92(1): 264–68.

[30] Hayashi Tet al: Walking to work and the risk for hypertension in men: The Osaka Health Survey. *Annals of Internal Medicine*, 1999;131: 21–26.

[31] Iwane M, Arita M, Tomimoto S et al: Walking 10,000 steps/day or more reduces blood pressure and sympathetic nerve activity in mild essential hypertension. *Hypertens Res*, 2000; 23(6): 573–80.

[32] Martin JE, Dubbert PM, Cushman WC: Controlled trial of aerobic exercise in hypertension. *Circulation*, 1990; 81(5): 1560-67.

INDEX

A

B

C

D

E

F

G

H

I

J

K

L

M

N

O

P

R

S

T

U

V

W